MADAM & EVE

TAKE US TO YOUR LEADER

BY STEPHEN FRANCIS & RICO

JACANA

For our wives, Bronwyn and Danya, for putting up with the daily circus that is the life of a cartoonist
– and for Stephen's father, age 99 years young

Published in 2016 in South Africa by
Jacana Media
10 Orange Street, Auckland Park, 2092
PO Box 291784, Melville, 2109
www.jacana.co.za

ISBN 978-1-4314-2430-6
Job number 002826
Printed and bound by ABC Press, Cape Town

OTHER MADAM & EVE BOOKS

Madam & Eve Collection   (Rapid Phase, 1993, reprint 1999)
Free At Last   (Penguin Books, 1994)
All Aboard for the Gravy Train   (Penguin Books, 1995)
Somewhere over the Rainbow Nation   (Penguin Books, 1996)
Madam & Eve's Greatest Hits   (Penguin Books, 1997)
Madams are from Mars, Maids are from Venus   (Penguin Books, 1997)
It's a Jungle Out There   (David Philip, 1998)
International Maid of Mystery   (David Philip, 1999)
Has anyone seen my Vibrating Cellphone?   (interactive.Africa, 2000)
The Madams are Restless   (Rapid Phase, 2000)
Crouching Madam, Hidden Maid   (Rapid Phase, 2001)
Madam & Eve, 10 Wonderful Years   (Rapid Phase, 2002)
The Maidtrix   (Rapid Phase, 2003)
Gin & Tonic for the Soul   (Rapid Phase, 2004)
Desperate Housemaids   (Rapid Phase, 2005)
Madams of the Caribbean   (Rapid Phase, 2006)
Bring me my (new) Washing Machine   (Rapid Phase, 2007)
Madam & Eve Unplugged   (Rapid Phase, 2008)
Strike While The Iron Is Hot   (Jacana, 2009)

Twilight of the Vuvuzelas   (Jacana, 2010)
Mother Anderson's Secret Book of Wit & Wisdom   (Jacana, 2011)
The Pothole at the End of the Rainbow   (Jacana, 2011)
Twenty   (Jacana, 2012)
Keep Calm and Take Another Tea Break   (Jacana, 2013)
Send in the Clowns   (Jacana, 2014)
Shed Happens   (Jacana, 2015)
Jamen sort kaffe er pa mode nu, Madam!   (Gyldendal, Denmark, 1995)
Jeg gyver Mandela Skylden for det her!   (Gyldendal, Denmark, 1995)
Alt under kontrol I Sydafrika!   (Bogfabrikken, Denmark, 1997)
Men alla dricker kaffet svart nufortiden, Madam!   (Bokfabrikken, Sweden, 1998)
Madame & Eve, Enfin Libres!   (Vents D'Ouest, France, 1997)
Votez Madame & Eve   (Vents D'Ouest, France, 1997)
La coupe est pleine   (Vents D'Ouest, France, 1998)
Rennue-Ménage à deux   (Vents D'Ouest, France, 1999)
En voient de toutes les couleurs   (Vents D'Ouest, France, 2000)
Madame vient de Mars, Eve de Venus   (Vents D'Ouest, France, 2000)
Madam & Eve   (LIKE, Finland, 2005)

MADAM & EVE APPEARS REGULARLY IN:
Mail & Guardian, The Star, Saturday Star, Herald, Mercury, Witness, Daily Dispatch, Cape Times, Pretoria News, Diamond Fields Advertiser, Die Volksblad, EC Today, Kokstad Advertiser, The Namibian.

TO CONTACT MADAM & EVE:
PO Box 413667, Craighall 2024, Johannesburg, South Africa
ricos@rico.co.za
www.madamandeve.co.za

THEY SAY THERE'S GOING TO BE ANOTHER CABINET RESHUFFLE. I'M GOING TO PREDICT THE RESULTS WITH **TAROT CARDS**.

HOW'S IT GOING SO FAR?

LET'S SEE... "THE EMPEROR", "THE TOWER", "THE WHEEL OF FORTUNE", "THE FOOL"... AND A BUNCH OF "CUPS."

WHAT'S IT MEAN?

ANYONE WHO THINKS THE **EMPEROR** IS GOING TO PAY BACK THE **MONEY** IS EITHER A **FOOL** OR IN THEIR **CUPS**.

SLAM!

MAYBE A LITTLE RE-READING IS IN ORDER.

TAROT FOR DUMMIES

IT SAYS HERE THAT WE HAVE SOME OF THE BEST **SOLAR POWER** POTENTIAL IN THE WORLD.

...SO WHY DOES THE GOVERNMENT WANT TO BUILD EXPENSIVE **NUCLEAR POWER PLANTS** INSTEAD?

...IS THERE EVEN ENOUGH **URANIUM** IN SOUTH AFRICA?

NO IDEA...

...BUT THERE'S NO SHORTAGE OF **GREEDIUM** AND **STUPIDIUM**.

MOM!!

AND IN OTHER NEWS, SABC CHIEF OPERATING OFFICER **HLAUDI MOTSOENENG** HAS SAID THE **MEDIA** NEEDS TO BE BETTER **REGULATED**.

HE SAID "IF THEY SHOW **CRIME** ON TV, PEOPLE WATCH AND WILL COMMIT **CRIME**."

"IF THEY SHOW **CORRUPTION**, PEOPLE WATCH AND WANT TO COMMIT **CORRUPTION**."

WHAT IF THEY SHOW **HONESTY** AND **HARD WORK**?

...PEOPLE WANT TO CHANGE THE CHANNEL.

MOM!!

AND NOW, IT'S TIME FOR ANOTHER EPISODE OF **SOUTH AFRICA'S GOT TALENT!** SO PLEASE WELCOME TONIGHT'S FIRST INCREDIBLY TALENTED NEW CONTESTANT...

...PRESIDENT JACOB ZUMA!

PRESIDENT ZUMA... LET'S TALK ABOUT YOUR INCREDIBLE **TALENT!** ...WHAT EXACTLY **IS** IT?

WELL, BOB -- BASICALLY I CAN DO **WHATEVER** I WANT, **WHENEVER** I WANT... AND THERE'S ABSOLUTELY **NOBODY** AROUND TO **STOP** ME!

WHAT ABOUT THE **TAXPAYERS?**

...WHO?

BWAHAHA! HA HA HAHA!

HEE HEE HEE! HO HO HO HO! HA HA HA HA!

SEE HOW I'M **LAUGHING** RIGHT NOW? ...AND IT'S NOT EVEN **FUNNY.**

HEEHEEHEE!

HEY! - I GOT A GOOD ONE: WHY DID THE CHICKEN **CROSS** THE **ROAD?**

I DON'T KNOW.

©RAPID PHASE-2015

...TO GET A THREE MILLION RAND **SECURITY UPGRADE.**

HEEHEEHEE!

A HUMOUR CONSULTANT **SOLD** ME THAT JOKE FOR A **MILLION** BUCKS.

HEH!HEH!HEH!

AND I'LL TELL YOU, THAT'S THE LAST TIME I'D DOING BUSINESS WITH MY **COUSIN.**

HEEHEEHEEHEE!

GWEN!!

EDITH ANDERSON INTERVIEWS FOR THE VACANT PRESIDENTIAL SPOKESPERSON JOB.

16

 MADAM & EVE'S **NEW SOUTH AFRICAN EMOJIS**

BY STEPHEN FRANCIS & RICO

Madam	Gogo	Gin & Tonic	Katty
Eve	Thandi	Dog eating homework	Mielie Lady
Hijacker			

 Eskom

 Taxpayer's money

 Nkandla

 Point of order!

 I don't recognise you!

 Mister President

 Guptas

 Gupta jet

 Mister Minister

 Hlaudi

 Pothole

 Minibus taxi

 Blue light convoy

 Traffic cop

 "cold drink"

 Bafana Bafana

The wors is ready

 Shark!

 Beggar

 Das Auto

 Sad Rand

 Prisoner Krejcir

 Correctional officer

 Springboks lose

 Springboks win!

21

MADAM & Eve

BY STEPHEN FRANCIS & RICO

HELLO. MY NAME IS GWEN... AND I SUFFER FROM PSA.

...PHONE SEPARATION ANXIETY.

HI GWEN!

HI GWEN!

...I ALSO SUFFER FROM FOBO: FEAR OF BEING OFFLINE.

IT WAS FINE AT FIRST. I USED TO CHECK MY PHONE ONLY A COUPLE OF TIMES A DAY. THEN ... EVERY HOUR ...THEN EVERY TEN MINUTES!

NEXT THING I KNEW, I WAS TWEETING, FACEBOOKING, INSTA- GRAMMING AND GOOGLING UNCONTROLLABLY!

I EVEN DISCOVERED THAT 77% OF ALL SOUTH AFRICANS CHECK THEIR PHONES ALL THE TIME FOR NO APPARENT REASON -- 77 PERCENT!

BUT NOW...THANKS TO SUPPORT GROUPS LIKE THIS... I HAVEN'T CHECKED MY PHONE IN ...15 WHOLE MINUTES! ...THANK YOU!

© RAPID PHASE - 2015

TIC TIC TIC TIC TIC
TIC TIC TIC TIC TIC TIC TIC TIC
TIC TIC TIC TIC TIC TIC TIC

HEY! SHE'S RIGHT. IT IS 77%!

click!

WHERE AM I?

IS THAT AN APPLE WATCH?

ANYBODY KNOW IF I CAN CHARGE MY PHONE HERE?

I JUST HIT LEVEL 165 ON "CANDY CRUSH."

I CAN'T TALK RIGHT NOW. I'M IN A SUPPORT GROUP.

25

MADAM & Eve

SHORTAGES

BY STEPHEN FRANCIS & RICO

WATER SHORTAGE

POWER SHORTAGE

#@%@# ESKOM.

TRY SHORTAGE

NEW ZEALAND 20
SOUTH AFRICA 18

TEMPER SHORTAGE

HOOT! HOOT! HOOT! HOOT! HOOT! HOOT! HOOT!
ECO MOBILITY

ENERGY SHORTAGE

HOUSING SHORTAGE

ECONOMIC FREEDOM SHORTAGE

ECONOMIC FREEDOM NOW!

STOCK EXCHANG

EFF

© RAPID PHASE - 2015

SENSE OF HUMOUR SHORTAGE

STUDENTS MUST FALL! HAHAHA!

G#%@)!!

I.Q. SHORTAGE

SEVENTY HUNDRED AND ONE HUNDRED... UH... TWENTY THIRTEEN THOUSAND... UH... AND ELEVENTY MILLION... UH...

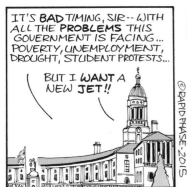

DOLUS EVENTUALIS

DOLUS NAUSEOUS

...WE'RE **BACK** WITH **MORE** IN-DEPTH **COVERAGE** OF THE **OSCAR PISTORIUS** APPEAL!

DOLUS EVICTUS

SLAM!!

HEY!!

DOLUS BLOTTUS

THE NOMINEES ARE...

"JAIL" -- A TALE OF REMORSE AND POSSIBLE REDEMPTION SET AGAINST THE BACKGROUND OF LIFE IN A SOUTH AFRICAN PRISON.

"UNCLE'S HOUSE" -- A TALE OF REMORSE AND POSSIBLE REDEMPTION SET AGAINST THE BACKGROUND OF LIFE IN AN UPSCALE PRETORIA MANSION.

AND THE **OSCAR** GOES TO...

SORRY. YOU'LL HAVE TO **WAIT**. WE'RE **RESERVING** JUDGEMENT.

WHAT'S ON OAF?

AN "OAF?"

MY **TEACHER** SAID PRESIDENT ZUMA TOOK "THE **OAF** OF OFFICE."

OATH! "...OATH OF OFFICE."

OH.

ALTHOUGH, COME TO **THINK** OF IT...

MOM!!

THIS IS YOUR DISGRUNTLED CAPTAIN SPEAKING. WELCOME ABOARD **SAA** FLIGHT "DUDU MYENI" TO **TAXPAYER BAILOUT**... WITH STOPOVERS AT **BANKRUPTCY** AND **INCOMPETENCE**.

YOU MAY EXPERIENCE SEVERE **TURBULENCE** DUE TO **TENDER IRREGULARITIES**, **MISMANAGEMENT** AND CHRONIC **ARROGANCE**.

SHOULD THIS INDUCE FEELINGS OF **DISGUST** AND **REVULSION**, YOU MAY WANT TO USE THE **AIR SICKNESS BAGS** IN FRONT OF YOU.

BLECCH!

I DON'T THINK THE CAPTAIN MEANT THAT **LITERALLY**, MOM.

WHEN **PRESIDENT ZUMA** WAS ASKED RECENTLY IF HE WOULD STAND FOR A **THIRD TERM**... MANY IN THE CROWD MADE A **FINGER** GESTURE...

...HOLDING UP **THREE** FINGERS, SUGGESTING THEIR **SUPPORT**.

NEVER JUDGE A NEWS SOUNDBITE UNTIL THE SENTENCE IS **OVER**.

...COMING UP NEXT... A PANEL DISCUSSION ON **WHITES** AND "**WHITENESS**" IN SOUTH AFRICA.

YOU'RE WHITE.

WELL... ACTUALLY MORE LIKE **PINK**... WITH A LITTLE **BLUE** COLOURING ... AND MAYBE A COUPLE OF **BROWN** SPOTS.

SLAM!!

NOW WHAT DID I _SAY_?!

FRY, THE BELOVED COUNTRY

JACK & JILL WENT UP THE HILL TO FETCH A PAIL OF **WATER**...

THE COPS PULLED A **RAID** THREW A STUN **GRENADE**

JACK FELL **DOWN** AND BROKE HIS **CROWN**...

AND THEY BOTH WERE INCARCERATED FOR CONTRAVENING THE NEW **WATER RESTRICTIONS** BYLAWS BECAUSE OF THE **DROUGHT**.

THE END

HEY! THAT'S **NOT** HOW IT GOES!

WELCOME TO THE NEW **REALITY**.

MOM!!

EVERYONE FREEZE!! PUT YOUR HANDS UP AND **DROP** THOSE PAPER CUPS!

...AND STEP **AWAY** FROM THAT **WATER COOLER!**

I REALLY HOPE IT **RAINS** SOON.

ME TOO.

BY STEPHEN FRANCIS & RICO

SOUTH AFRICAN AIRWAYS
AIRPORT TARMAC SIGNALS

Turn left.

STOP!
Gupta jet
landing!

Disgruntled SAA pilots
on your right.

HELP! Deep pothole
on runway!

Dudu Myeni is my
cousin/friend/neighbour.

HEY! Get that parking
guard out of here!

Anybody know what the #$%# is
going on with the Airbus contract?

Uh-oh. SAA is broke.

Taxpayer bailout money
coming through.

OMG!
Is that
Zuma's
new jet?!

MADAM & EVE

BY STEPHEN FRANIS & RICO

SOUTH AFRICAN COLLECTIVE NOUNS FOR 2016

A TWITTER OF RACISTS

A WEALTH OF MINISTERS

A FLEECE OF AIRBUSES

A HOOTING OF TAXIS

A KICK-BACK OF NUCLEAR DEALS

A NAP OF PARLIAMENTARIANS

A POACH OF RHINOS

A DISAPPOINTMENT OF MATRIC RESULTS

A CLUSTER EFF

A **BAVUMA** OF RUNS

53

LIFESIZE EMOJIS! YOU CAN BE MY FIRST **INVESTOR**!

SLAM!! FINE! GO AHEAD AND DISCOURAGE ENTREPRENEURIAL SPIRIT!

YOU DIDN'T DO YOUR HOMEWORK **AGAIN**, THANDI?

NO, MISS...

BUT AS YOU CAN SEE... I'M REALLY **UPSET** ABOUT IT.

LIFESIZE EMOJIS! WE'RE GOING TO BE **RICH**!

PRINCI

IT'S AMAZING HOW MANY GREAT **HOME MANAGEMENT IDEAS** ONE CAN GET SIMPLY BY PERUSING THE **INTERNET**.

EVE! THE DISHES ARE STILL IN THE **SINK**!!

KICK!!

WHAT **IDEA** WAS THAT?

"...KICKSTARTER."

G#%@)!!

58

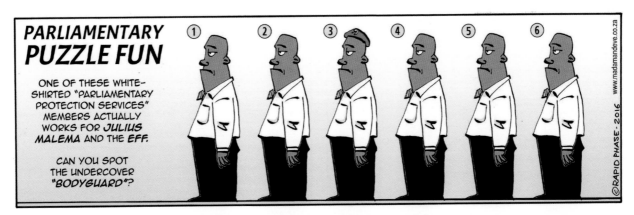

67

SMILING BUDDHA

LAUGHING ZUMA

HEH HEH HEH HEH HEH HEH HEH HEH HEH HEH HEH

Sticks to ANYTHING! ...even TEFLON!

Holds fast for over SEVEN YEARS!

Won't APPEAL off! (Hopefully)

May eventually put the CELL back in CELLotape.

Spy Tape*

*Transparent version discontinued

JUST ONCE I'D LIKE TO PICK UP MY MORNING NEWSPAPER AND **NOT** READ A STORY ABOUT CORRUPTION, NEPOTISM, RACISM, CRIME ... OR THE FALLING RAND!

SLAM!!
YOU **TRY** TO DO SOMEONE A **FAVOUR!**

MADAM & Eve

BY STEPHEN FRANCIS & RICO

SOUTH AFRICAN
EDITIONS OF
DR SEUSS
AND OTHER CLASSIC
CHILDRENS' BOOKS
FOR 2016

MADAM & EVE'S DR SEUSS BOOKS FOR SOUTH AFRICA 2016

MADAM & EVE'S DR SEUSS BOOKS FOR SOUTH AFRICA 2016

MADAM & EVE'S DR SEUSS BOOKS FOR SOUTH AFRICA 2016

TEA BREAK

TEA BREAKING AND ENTERING

TEA BREAKING BAD

TEA BREAK DANCING

MADAM & EVE's

SOUTH AFRICAN
**OLYMPIC
EVENTS**

SYNCHRONISED SMASH & GRAB

SQUASH

MADAM & EVE's

SOUTH AFRICAN
**OLYMPIC
EVENTS**

ELECTRIC FENCE POLE VAULT

HORIZONTAL BAR

MADAM &Eve

BY STEPHEN FRANCIS & RICO

Pokémon GO

| POKEMON **GO FAST** | POKEMON **GO SLOW** | POKEMON **GO DRINK** | POKEMON **GO GIGGLE** |

HOME AFFAIRS

HEH. HEH. HEH. HEH.

| POKEMON **GO PROTEST** | POKEMON **GO CENSOR** | POKEMON **GO VOTE** | POKEMON **GO AWAY** |

SERVICE DELIVERY NOW!

© RAPID PHASE - 2016

SABC NEWS

IEC

SLAM!!

Affordable luxury fit for a president.

Goes from zero to eleventy in something seconds.

Reverses so quickly, you can't help but giggle.

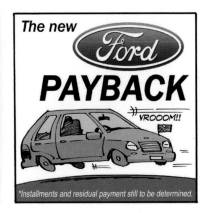

The new **Ford** **PAYBACK**

VROOOM!!

Installments and residual payment still to be determined.

MISTER PRESIDENT! MISTER PRESIDENT!

...AND, AS AN ADDITIONAL **COST-CUTTING** MEASURE...

...FROM NOW ON, ALL THOSE EXPENSIVE **OVERSEAS TRIPS** AND LAVISH **DINNER PARTIES** WILL HAVE TO BE SERIOUSLY **MOTIVATED.**

AND WHAT WILL THE NEW "MOTIVATIONAL GUIDELINES" BE, MISTER PRESIDENT?

DON'T ASK **ME**. ASK THE NEW **MINISTER** OF **MOTIVATION**... AS SOON AS I **APPOINT** ONE.

AFTER THE **SONA** SPEECH, PRESIDENT ZUMA'S LIMO DRIVER SUDDENLY REGRETS SUGGESTING CHICKEN TAKE-AWAYS AS A NEW **COST-CUTTING** MEASURE.

UH-OH.

KFC

POINT OF ORDER

MENU

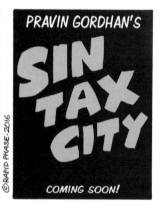

HE'S BACK!

...and this time he's trapped on an even **WORSE** planet!

MADAM & Eve

BY STEPHEN FRANCIS & RICO

WELL, THAT WAS THE NEWS... NOW LET'S CHECK OUT THE LATEST **PRESIDENTIAL WEATHER REPORT**...

AS YOU CAN SEE... MORE BIG STORM CLOUDS LOOMING IN THE **ZUMA WEATHER SYSTEM**.

THE POLITICAL CLIMATE CONTINUES TO GROW **HOTTER** WITH THREATENING DARK **SPY TAPE** CLOUDS FORMING OVER THE PRESIDENT, CAUSING A LACK OF **TRANSPARENCY**.

...AND DESPITE **CLEARING** OF RECENT **NO CONFIDENCE** COLD FRONTS, HIGH DISCONTENT PRESSURE SYSTEMS PERSIST...

...RESULTING IN WIDESPREAD RISING PRICES, FALLING RANDS AND CATASTROPHIC **JOB DROUGHT** CONDITIONS...

...ACCOMPANIED BY A HUGE BREAKING OF **WIND**, CAUSING ALL LOOSE SPIN DOCTORS, NOT NAILED DOWN, TO RUN FOR COVER.

...IT LOOKS LIKE A **SLEET STORM** AHEAD FOR PRESIDENT ZUMA FOR THE REST OF HIS TERM.

...ALTHOUGH, AS YOU CAN SEE, IN **SOME** AREAS HE STILL HAS SOME **FANS**.

©RAPID PHASE - 2016

WHAT HAPPENS WHEN THE **SLEET** HITS THE **FANS**?

MOM!! I'M **LISTENING** TO THIS!!

MADAM & Eve

BY STEPHEN FRANCIS & RICO

AFTER THE HAWKS

(NEW SOUTH AFRICAN METAPHORICAL ANIMAL/MAMMAL INVESTIGATIVE ORGANISATIONS)

SQUAWK!

THE BATS

TASKED WITH INVESTIGATING INTERNATIONAL CRICKET MATCH FIXING.

THE PHISH

NIGERIAN E-MAIL COMPUTER SCAMS DON'T STAND A CHANCE AGAINST THESE GUYS!

THE SAGITTARIANS

ABLE TO IMMEDIATELY **ARREST** ANYONE IN A BAR USING "WHAT'S YOUR SIGN?" AS A PICK UP LINE.

THE SCAPEGOATS

INVESTIGATING ANY AND ALL WATERKLOOF AIRPORT STAFF WHO ALLOW AEROPLANES LANDING TO ATTEND **GUPTA** WEDDING PARTIES.

BAAA!

THE CHAUVINIST PIGS

ON THE TRAIL OF SEXUAL HARASSMENT IN THE WORKPLACE.

© RAPID PHASE - 2016

THE PORCUPINES

CRACKING DOWN ON EXCESSIVE USE OF **POINTS** OF ORDER OR **POINTS** OF PRIVILEGE.

EFF

THE SLOTHS

TOO **LAZY** TO INVESTIGATE ANYONE.

ZZZZ

THE DUNG BEETLES

A CONTINUING INVESTIGATION OF **JACOB ZUMA** ... BUT IT'S AN <u>UPHILL</u> BATTLE.

ZUPTALCION ™

SIDE EFFECTS may include:
- Accumulation of surprising, unexpected wealth.
- Your name in media head-lines.
- Invitations to all government functions, weddings and contract tenders.

MADAM & Eve

BY STEPHEN FRANCIS & RICO

HELLO. MY NAME IS JACOB...

...AND I'M A GUPTAHOLIC. **HI JACOB!!**

IT ALL STARTED YEARS AGO... THE BROTHERS GAVE ME SOME SMALL **LOANS**...THE **FIRST** ONE WAS **INTEREST-FREE**.

NEXT THING I KNEW, I WAS **HOOKED**. WE BECAME **CO-DEPENDENTS**... "HELPING" EACH OTHER. THEY EVEN HAD MY NUMBER ON **SPEED-DIAL**!

OH YEAH! WE'VE ALL BEEN THERE!

I LOOKED AFTER THEIR BUSINESSES... AND THEY GAVE MY WIFE A **JOB**! ...**AND MY DAUGHTER**! THEY EVEN MADE MY **SON** A **COMPANY DIRECTOR**!

THEN... I WOKE UP ONE MORNING...TO DISCOVER I HAD ALLOWED THEIR **WEDDING GUESTS** TO LAND AT A **MILITARY AIRPORT**!

THAT'S WHEN I REALISED THE **STATE** WAS **CAPTURED**. THEY WERE EVEN...>CHOKE< ...OFFERING THEIR FRIENDS **MINISTERIAL POSITIONS**!

© RAPID PHASE - 2016

BUT NOW, THANKS TO **GUPTAHOLICS ANONYMOUS**... I'VE BEEN LIVING A GUPTA-FREE LIFE FOR 12 DAYS AND 36 HOURS.

>CLAP!< >CLAP!< >CLAP!< >CLAP!< >CLAP!< >CLAP!<

...ER... AND THE FACT THAT THEY **LEFT** IN THE MIDDLE OF THE **NIGHT**, WITHOUT EVEN SAYING **GOODBYE**.

THANK YOU FOR SHARING, JACOB. WHO'S **NEXT**?

...DUDUZANE?

NO...I'M NOT READY.

DES?   ...NOT NOW.

FIKILE?   UH...

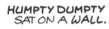

AND IN OTHER NEWS... **PRESIDENT ZUMA** CELEBRATED HIS BIRTHDAY ON TUESDAY.

HE SAID HIS ONE WISH... IS TO SEE SOUTH AFRICA BECOME A **BETTER COUNTRY.**

HOW DO YOU THINK HE COULD **MAKE** THIS A **BETTER** COUNTRY?

...OH.

WHAT'S WRONG, MISTER PRESIDENT? YOU'RE **SWEATING** AND **SHAKING!**

I- I'VE BEEN **SPEED DIALLING** THIS NUMBER AND NO ONE PICKS UP!

...AND NO ONE IN MY **FAMILY** HAS BEEN OFFERED A **JOB** OR A **LOAN** IN WEEKS!

AND THAT'S NOT **ALL!** NO ONE'S EVEN COME **CLOSE** TO HELPING OR BAILING ME OUT!!

⹂CHOKE!⹂ IT'S BEEN **TEN** WHOLE **DAYS** SINCE THEY **LEFT!**

... **GUPTA** WITHDRAWAL.

AND IN OTHER NEWS... A BOLD **PLAN** IS **REPORTEDLY** BEING CRAFTED BY THE **ANC** TO **REMOVE** PRESIDENT ZUMA **QUICKLY** AND **EFFICIENTLY** IMMEDIATELY AFTER THE LOCAL ELECTIONS.

...ALTHOUGH DETAILS OF THE "EXIT PLAN" REMAIN A **SECRET.**

WE'RE READY FOR A PRACTICE RUN, MISTER PRESIDENT.

NOW?!

MADAM & Eve

BY STEPHEN FRANCIS & RICO

AND IN OTHER NEWS... A CASE OF **TREASON** HAD BEEN OPENED UP AGAINST **JULIUS MALEMA**... FOR HIS INTERVIEW WITH AL JAZEERA...

YES!

...SOMEONE SHOULD CALL THIS **AL JAZEERA** GUY AND **THANK** HIM.

PERFECT TIMING, MISTER PRESIDENT...WE'VE PUT TOGETHER A NEW **TV SPOT** FOR YOUR **P.R. CAMPAIGN!** TAKE A LOOK!

JULIUS MALEMA, THE *FIREBRAND.*

...WHERE THERE'S **SMOKE,** THERE'S **FIRE.**

...HE'S *INCENDIARY.*

...*INFLAMMATORY.*

AND HIS FAVOURITE COLOUR IS... **RED.**

SURE, **JACOB ZUMA** MAY HAVE MADE A FEW *MISTAKES.*

BUT... HAVE YOU STOPPED TO THINK OF THE *ALTERNATIVE?*

PRESIDENT ZUMA

BETTER THE DEVIL YOU *KNOW.*

@RAPID PHASE · 2016

...THAN THE DEVIL YOU *DON'T.*

...PAID FOR BY FRIENDS OF JACOB ZUMA.

I LOVE IT!

WHAT THE HELL. IT KIND OF MAKES SENSE... IN A WEIRD KIND OF WAY.

MOM!!

≧SIGH≦ FIRST THE **NKANDLA** RULING... NOW THE SPY TAPES **CORRUPTION CHARGES** JUDGEMENT!!

EVERYTHING IS SUDDENLY GOING **AGAINST** ME! WHAT DID I **DO** TO **DESERVE** THIS?!

WELL...

IT COULD BE THE FAULT OF **KARMA**, SIR.

©RAPID PHASE - 2016

THE **KARMAS**?! ...NOT **ANOTHER** INDIAN FAMILY!!

YOU EXPLAIN IT.

CAN YOU HELP ME WITH MY ENGLISH HOMEWORK? I NEED FIVE EXAMPLES OF **OXYMORONS**.

©RAPID PHASE - 2016   www.madamandeve.co.za

"AIRLINE FOOD."

"MINISTERIAL INTEGRITY."

"METRORAIL SCHEDULE."

"PRESIDENTIAL APOLOGY"...UH...

..."WORKER'S DAY."

HAHA! **VERY** FUNNY!

JUJU'S DIARY:

Eat some **PESTO**.

Choose a **VESTO**.

©RAPID PHASE - 2016   www.madamandeve.co.za

Grab a **RESTO**.

ZZZZZZ

MANIFESTO!

I AM THE **BESTO**.

WE'RE LEARNING ABOUT **MOSES** IN BIBLE CLASS TOMORROW.

THAT'S NICE.

IS IT TRUE **MOSES** HAD A **STAFF?**

YES... A **DOMESTIC WORKER** AND LOTS OF **BODYGUARDS.**

MOM!

THEY SAY MOSES **PARTED** THE **RED SEA.**

COMPLETELY **TRUE.**

SO BASICALLY, MOSES WAS...

THE NEW HEAD OF PARLIAMENTARY SECURITY.

MOM!!

I'M CONFUSED. WAS MOSES BLACK... OR WHITE?

BOTH. ...WHITE **SHIRT** ...WITH BLACK **PANTS.**

≥SIGH!≤

I'M TOLD **MOSES** LED THE **EXODUS.** ...WHAT'S AN "EXODUS?"

SLAM!!

MAYBE I ASK TOO MANY QUESTIONS.

CAUTION
PROTECTED BY
GAME OF THRONES
ARMED RESPONSE

CAUTION
PROTECTED BY
WALKING DEAD
ARMED RESPONSE

Four signs that your home security needs an upgrade.

1. Your doors don't lock properly.
2. Your alarm system is never tested.

3. Your motion detectors break frequently.

4. There's a strange man walking behind you carrying away your brand new TV set.

TSHWANE POLITICAL PROTEST.

IF YOU **DRINK** WHILE DRIVING... DO THEY TAKE AWAY YOUR **DRIVER'S LICENSE?**

YES.

IF YOU **DRINK** WHILE WATCHING **SABC**... DO THEY TAKE AWAY YOUR **TV** LICENSE?

HEE HEE! HAHAHA!

HAHAHA! HOHOHO!

I DON'T GET IT.

WE DON'T **HAVE A** TV LICENSE!

THE FOLLOWING PROGRAMME CONTAINS **NO VIOLENCE,** NO BAD LANGUAGE OR **ADULT** SITUATIONS...

... AND CONTAINS ABSOLUTELY **NO** INFORMATION THAT MAY CAUSE **OFFENSE** AMONGST **VIEWERS.**

WHAT **KIND** OF PROGRAMME IS **THAT?**

WELCOME TO **SABC NEWS.** TODAY'S TOP STORY...

www.madamandeve.co.za

©RAPID PHASE - 2016

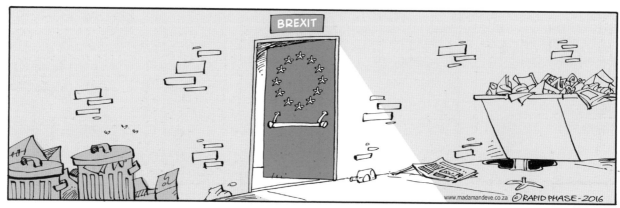

TODAY'S TOP STORY... THE TREASURY HAS SAID THAT **PRESIDENT ZUMA** MUST **PAY** BACK **7.8 MILLION RAND** OF THE **R246 MILLION** UPGRADES DONE TO HIS **NKANDLA** HOMESTEAD.

7.8 MILLION?! THAT'S **ALL**?!

R 7.8 MILLION?! THAT **MUCH**?!

≈ SIGH. ≈

TIC TIC TIC TIC

HELLO, **GUPTA** HOLDINGS. HOW MAY I DIRECT YOUR CALL?

THIS IS JACOB ZUMA... GET ME **AJAY** OR **ATUL** RIGHT AWAY!

...AND WHAT MAY I SAY THIS IS IN REFERENCE TO?

TELL THEM I NEED TO **BORROW** 7.8 MILLION RANDS **ASAP**.

I'LL SEE IF THEY ARE AVAILABLE. PLEASE HOLD...

♫ RAINDROPS KEEP FALLING ON MY HEAD... ♫

ALL OUR AGENTS ARE STILL BUSY. PLEASE HOLD. ...YOUR CALL IS VALUABLE TO US.

© RAPID PHASE · 2016

♫ RAINDROPS KEEP FALLING ON MY HEAD... ♫

ALL OUR AGENTS ARE STILL BUSY. PLEASE HOLD. ...YOUR CALL IS VALUABLE TO US.

♫ ...BUT THAT DOESN'T MEAN MY EYES WILL SOON BE TURNING RED... ♫

6#%@!!

HEY! AREN'T YOU SUPPOSED TO BE IN SCHOOL TODAY?!

THEY SENT ME HOME FOR FIGHTING ON THE PLAYGROUND.

WHAT?!

ONE OF THE BOYS CALLED ME A NAME. SO I GAVE HIM A MASIPA.

WHAT'S A MASIPA?

... A SLAP ON THE WRIST.

MADAM! I NEED SOME MONEY! I'M ALMOST OUT OF PHONE AIRTIME!

CAN'T YOU WAIT? I'M IN THE BATHROOM!

NO CAN DO! WE'RE LEAVING FOR THE SHOPS NOW.

¡SIGH¡ OKAY... HERE'S 20 BUCKS. I'M SLIPPING IT UNDER THE DOOR.

... GIVES NEW MEANING TO THE TERM "PAY AS YOU GO."

I HEARD THAT!

TODAY'S TOP STORY: BUSINESS LEADERS ARE INCREASINGLY CONCERNED OVER THE CREAKING INFRASTRUCTURE OF FINANCIAL MARKETS...

((CREAK! POP! ((CREEEAK! POP! ✷

THE FINANCIAL MARKETS ARE COLLAPSING!!

... WHAT?

((CREAK!))

122

HEH. HEH. HEH.

WE DIDN'T KNOW YOU LIKED **POKEMON GO**, MISTER PRESIDENT.

I DON'T.

BUT ALL THE "**POKEMON GO**" PUBLICITY IS A USEFUL DISTRACTION.

DISTRACTION? FROM **WHAT**?

... ALL THE "**ZUMA** MUST **GO**" PUBLICITY.

HE'S GOT A POINT.

126

MADAM & EVE'S
SHAKESPEARE
SOUTH AFRICA
2016

BY STEPHEN FRANCIS & RICO

"NOW IS THE WINTER OF OUR DISCONTENT."

VOTE

VOTING STATION

"SOMETHING IS ROTTEN IN THE STATE OF AUCKLAND PARK."

TO CENSOR, OR NOT TO CENSOR: THAT IS THE QUESTION.

HLAUDI SABC

"DOUBLE, DOUBLE TOIL AND TROUBLE; POLITICIANS PROMISE, VOTERS GRUMBLE."

START THE LIMO!

"THE COURSE OF TRUE LOVE DID NEVER RUN SMOOTHLY."

EFF

VOTE EFF

VOTE ANC

"IF MUSIC IS THE FOOD OF LOVE, PLAY ON."
(AS LONG IT FOLLOWS A 90% SOUTH AFRICAN MUSIC QUOTA)

"NEITHER A BORROWER NOR A LENDER BE."

R

"IS THIS IS A POKEMON I SEE BEFORE ME?"

"THE DA DOTH PROTEST TOO MUCH METHINKS."

ANC

"OUT, DAMNED SPOT!"

SUPER CLEAN

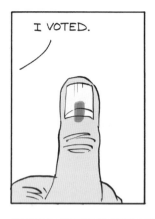

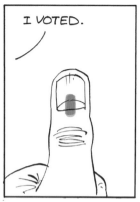

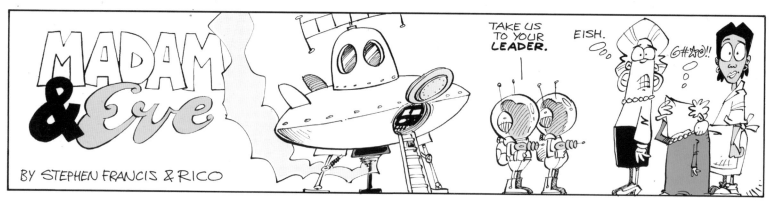